BOOK OF

SILLY

JOKES

p

This is a Parragon Book
First published in 2003

Parragon
Queen Street House
4 Queen Street
Bath BA1 1HE
UK

Produced by Magpie Books, an imprint of
Constable & Robinson Ltd, London

Illustrations © David Mostyn

ISBN 1-40540-620-8

A copy of the British Library Cataloguing-in-Publication Data
is available from the British Library

Printed in China

Contents

Bugs and Spiders

What is a termite's favorite breakfast?
Oak-meal.

What did one termite say to the other termite when he saw a house burning?
Barbecue tonight!

What do you call an amorous insect?
The Love Bug.

What do you call an insect that has just flown by?
A flu bug.

What did the termite say in the pub?
Is the bar tender here?

What did the termite say when he saw that his friends had completely eaten a chair?
Wooden you know it!

How do you keep flies out of the kitchen?
Put a bucket of manure in the lounge.

Which fly makes films?
Steven Spielbug.

Which fly captured the ladybird?
The dragon-fly.

Why did the firefly keep stealing things?
He was light-fingered.

What goes snap, crackle, pop?
A firefly with a short circuit.

How do fireflies start a race?
Ready, steady, glow!

What did one firefly say to another?
Got to glow now.

If there are five flies in the kitchen, which one is the American football player?
The one in the sugar bowl.

Why were the flies playing football in a saucer?
They were playing for the cup.

Waiter, I must say that I don't like all the flies in this dining room! Tell me which ones you don't like and I'll chase them out for you.

A little firefly was in school one day and he put up his hand.
"Please, miss, may I be excused?"
"Yes," replied the teacher, "when you've got to glow, you've got to glow."

How do you know if you have a
tough mosquito?
If you slap him, he slaps you back.

What has six legs, bites and talks
in code?
A morse-quito.

What's the difference between a
mosquito and a fly?
Try sewing buttons on a mosquito!

What's the difference between a lawyer and a mosquito?
A mosquito drops off you when you die.

Why is it best to be bitten quickly by one mosquito?
Because an itch in time saves nine.

Which is the most religious insect in the Middle East?
A mosque-ito.

What is small and gray, sucks blood and eats cheese?
A mouse-quito.

Why did the mosquito go to the dentist?
To improve his bite.

What wears a black cape, flies through the night and sucks blood?
A mosquito in a cape.

Why are mosquitoes religious?
They prey on you.

Why are mosquitoes annoying?
Because they get under your skin.

What do you get if you cross a
mosquito with a knight?
A bite in shining armor.

What's a mosquito's favorite song?
I've Got You Under My Skin.

What do you call A Tale of Two
Mosquitoes?
A bite-time story.

What did one mosquito say to
another when they came out of the
theater?
Fancy a bite?

What is a mosquito's favorite
sport?
Skin-diving.

What's the name of the opera
about a mouse and a flea?
Die Fleadermouse.

What did one amorous flea say to
the other?
I love you aw-flea.

What is the insect family's favorite
game?
Cricket.

How do we know that insects have
amazing brains?
Because they always know when
you're having a picnic.

What lives in gum trees?
Stick insects.

What is the best insect chat-up line?
Pardon me, but is this stool taken?

What happened to the man who turned into an insect?
He beetled off.

Moths – when will they learn that if a light is bright, then it probably isn't the moon?
And when it's my head they're smacking into then they'll soon meet a rolled-up newspaper.

Daddy Long Legs – oh look, a human, someone far bigger than I am. I know, I'll fly into them until I've annoyed them enough to kill me, then I'll do it some more until they've completed their mission.

Bees – shouldn't someone tell them that they'll die if they sting you?

Spiders – these are the animals that find their way into your bath, and then stay there. Why don't they get it into their heads that the bath is the last place they should explore?

Wasps – while everyone runs a mile when they see one, why does it take hours for them to work out how to get out of a room, even after you've opened the window that they're standing on?

Ants – so, they can carry ten times their own body weight! Thousands of years on this planet and they still haven't worked out how to build a truck!

Bluebottles – what is the point of their existence?
Don't they realise that if they insist on buzzing round your bedroom when you're trying to get some sleep that any minute now they'll have their buzzing stopped forever?

Snails – get an engine or something!

What do you call a nervous insect?
Jitterbug.

Who stole the sheets off the bed?
Bed buglars.

What do you call a top pop group
made up of nits?
The Lice Girls.

What car do insects drive?
A Volkswagen Beetle.

What do you say to an annoying
cockroach?
Stop bugging me!

What insect can fly underwater?
A bluebottle in a submarine.

What do you call an insect from outer space?
Bug Rogers.

What's a grasshopper's favorite band?
Buddy Holly and the Crickets.

What do you get if you cross a praying mantis with a termite?
A bug that says grace before eating your house.

What did one stick insect say to another?
Stick around.

Why is the letter "t" so important to a stick insect?
Without it, it would be a sick insect.

What do you call a mayfly with a
machine gun?
Baddy Long Legs.

What creepy crawlies do athletes
break?
Tapeworms.

Why did the termite eat a sofa and
two chairs?
It had a suite tooth.

How do you get rid of termites?
Exterminite them.

What lies down a hundred feet in
the air?
A dead centipede.

What kind of insects live on the
moon?
Lunar ticks.

What's the difference between
head lice and nits?
A real nit is too stupid to find your
head.

What's the difference between a
maggot and a cockroach?
Cockroaches crunch more when
you eat them.

How do insects travel when they go
on holiday?
They go for a buggy ride.

Why was the insect kicked out of the park?
It was a litterbug.

What do you call singing insects?
Humbugs.

What is an insect's favorite pop group?
The Beatles.

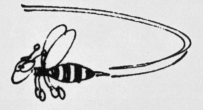

What do you get if you cross the
Lone Ranger with an insect?
The Masked-quito.

What has antlers and sucks your blood?
A moose-quito.

What do insects learn at school?
Mothematics.

What insect lives on nothing?
A moth, because it eats holes.

How can you make a moth ball?
Hit it with a fly swatter.

Where do butterflies hire their
dinner jackets?
Moth Bros.

What is pretty and delicate and
carries a sub-machine gun?
A killer butterfly.

How do you make a butterfly?
Flick it out of the dish with a
butter knife.

What do you get if you cross a
moth with a firefly?
An insect that can find its way
around a dark wardrobe.

How do stones stop moths eating
your clothes?
Because a rolling stone gathers no
moths.

What is a myth?
A female moth.

Why did the moth nibble a hole in
the carpet?
He wanted to see the floor show.

Who do all moths bow to?
The Moth-er Superior.

Why was the moth so unpopular?
He kept picking holes in
everything.

How does a microscopic insect say
goodbye?
It microwaves.

Why wouldn't they let the butterfly
into the dance?
Because it was a moth ball.

Why did the butterfly?
Because it saw the milk-float.

What circles the lampshade at
200 mph?
Stirling Moth.

What is the biggest moth?
A mam-moth.

What do bees do if they want to use public transport?
Wait at a buzz stop.

What's an English bee's favorite TV station?
The Bee-Bee C.

What does a queen bee do when she belches?
She issues a royal pardon.

How does a queen bee get around
the hive?
She's throne.

What's yellow and brown and
covered in blackberries?
A bramble bee.

What is more dangerous than
being with a fool?
Fooling with a bee.

Why did the bee start spouting poetry?
It was waxing lyrical.

Who is a bee's favorite composer?
Bee-thoven.

What did the mommy bee say to the naughty little bee?
Bee-hive yourself!

Can bees fly in the rain?
Not without their little yellow
jackets.

What goes hum-choo, hum-choo?
A bee with a cold.

What is a bee-line?
The shortest distance between two
buzz-stops.

What's the difference between a very old, shaggy Yeti and a dead bee?
One's a seedy beast and the other's a deceased bee.

Who wrote books for little bees?
Bee-trix Potter.

What do you call a bee who's had a spell put on him?
Bee-witched.

What has brown and yellow stripes
and buzzes along at the bottom of
the sea?
A bee in a submarine.

Why do bees hum?
Because they've forgotten the
words.

What kind of bee hums and drops
things?
A fumble bee.

What did the bee say to the
flower?
Hello, honey.

What are a bee's favorite flowers?
Bee-gonias.

What is brown and yellow and
buzzes at 36,000 feet in the air?
A bee in an airplane.

What did the confused bee say?
To bee or not to bee.

What are the cleverest bees?
Spelling bees.

Which bee is good for your health?
Vitamin bee.

What goes zzub, zzub?
A bee flying backwards.

Why do bees buzz?
They can't whistle.

Why did the bee have its legs
crossed as it flew?
It was looking for the BP station.

What bee can never be
understood?
A mumble bee.

What do you get if you cross a bee
with a quarter of a pound of
minced beef?
A humburger.

Who is a bee's favorite painter?
Pablo Beecasso.

What is a baby bee?
A little humbug.

What is a bee's favorite film?
The Sting.

Who is a wasp's favorite singer?
Rob-bee Williams.

What did the drone say to the
Queen Bee?
Swarm in here, isn't it?

Who's top of the charts in the beehive?
Sting.

What did the spider say to the bee?
Your honey or your life.

Where do bees keep their money?
In a honey-box.

Which is a bee's favorite pop group?
The Bee Gees.

What fly has laryngitis?
A hoarsefly.

What is a bee's favorite novel?
The Great Gats-bee.

What do you get if you cross a bee
with a door-bell?
A hum-dinger.

How many bees do you need in a
proper bee choir?
A humdred.

What does the bee Santa Claus
say at Christmas?
Ho-hum-hum.

Why did the bees go on strike?
Because they wanted more honey
and shorter working flowers.

Why do bees have sticky hair?
Because of the honey combs.

Where do bees come from?
Stingapore.

What kind of gum do bees chew?
Bumble-gum.

Which queen can never wear a
crown?
A queen bee.

Why did the queen bee kick all the
other bees out of the hive?
Because they kept droning on and
on.

What does a bee say before it
stings you?
This is going to hurt me much more
than it hurts you.

What do you call a bee that can
shelter a plane?
An aero-drone.

If bees make honey, what do
wasps make?
Waspberry jam.

Where do you take a sick wasp?
To waspital.

What is a wasp's favorite song?
Just a Spoonful of Sugar.

What did the bee say to the wasp
who tried to make honey?
Don't wasp your time!

Insect Films: The Fly; Batman; Beetlejuice; The Sting; The Good, the Bug and the Ugly; The Frog Prince; Four Webbings and a Funeral; Seven Bats for Seven Brothers.

What's the difference between a monster orangutan and a flea? A monster orangutan can have a flea but a flea can't have a monster orangutan.

What do you get if you cross a
witch with a flea?
Very worried dogs.

Collecting Mosquitoes – by Lara
Bites

Collecting Mosquitoes – by Ethan
Alive

While visiting close friends, a gnat,
Decided to sleep in a hat.
But an elderly guest
Decided to rest
Now the gnat and the hat are
   quite flat.

A fly and a flea in a flue
Were wondering what they should
   do.
Said the fly, "Let us flee!"
Said the flea, "Let us fly."
So they flew, through a flaw in the
   flue.

I say, I say, I say. What has a purple-spotted body, ten hairy legs and eyes on stalks?
I don't know.
Nor do I, but there's one creeping up your back!

Girl: Can you eat spiders?
Boy: Why?
Girl: One's just crawled into your sandwich.

Bluebottle: I must fly.
Bee: OK, I'll give you a buzz later.

Boy: Mom, mom, I've just
swallowed a spider.
Mom: Shall I get the doctor to give
you something for it?
Boy: No, let it starve to death.

Boy: Dad, dad, there's a spider in the bath.
Dad: What's wrong with that? You've seen spiders before.
Boy: Yes, but this one is three feet wide and using all the hot water!

What insect can be spelled with just one letter?
Bee.

Boy scout: I'm in agony. I've been stung by a bee.
Scout leader: Well, we'll put some cream on it.
Boy scout: You'll be lucky, it must be miles away now.

Father: Why did you put a toad in your sister's bed?
Son: I couldn't find a spider.

Teacher: What did Robert the
Bruce do after watching the
spider climbing up and down?
Pupil: He went and invented the
yo-yo.

Did you hear about the angry flea?
He was hopping mad.

Did you hear about the bloke who
set up a flea circus?
He started it from scratch.

Did you hear about the religious
moth?
He gave up woollens for lint.

Did you hear about the flea who
failed his exams?
He didn't come up to scratch.

Did you hear about the boy who
wanted to run away to the circus?
He ended up in a flea circus.

Knock Knock.
Who's there?
Weevil.
Weevil who?
Weevil work it out.

Knock Knock.
Who's there?
Flea.
Flea who?
Flea's a jolly good fellow.

Knock Knock.
Who's there?
Flea.
Flea who?
Flea thirty!

Knock Knock.
Who's there?
Spider.
Spider who?
Spider through the keyhole.

Knock Knock.
Who's there?
Webster.
Webster who?
Webster Spin, your friendly
neighborhood spider.

Knock Knock.
Who's there?
Mosquito.
Mosquito who?
Mosquito smoking soon.

Knock Knock.
Who's there?
Fly.
Fly who?
Fly away soon.

Knock Knock.
Who's there?
Moth.
Moth who?
Motht people know the anthwer.

Knock Knock.
Who's there?
Earwig.
Earwig who?
Earwig come!

Knock Knock.
Who's there?
Grub.
Grub who?
Grub hold of my hand and let's go!

Knock Knock.
Who's there?
Roach.
Roach who?
Roach out and touch somebody.

Knock Knock.
Who's there?
Bee.
Bee who?
Bee careful out there!

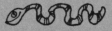

Knock Knock.
Who's there?
Termite.
Termite who?
Termite's the night!

Knock Knock.
Who's there?
Army Ant.
Army Ant who?
Army Ants coming for tea, then?

Knock Knock.
Who's there?
Larva.
Larva who?
Larva cup of coffee.

Knock Knock.
Who's there?
Amos.
Amos who?
Amosquito.

70

Knock Knock.
Who's there?
Anna.
Anna who?
Annather mosquito.

Knock Knock.
Who's there?
Insect.
Insect who?
Insect your name and address
   here.

Knock Knock.
Who's there?
Bug.
Bug who?
Bugsy Malone.

Knock Knock.
Who's there?
Tristan.
Tristan who?
Tristan insect to really get up your
  nose.

Doctor, doctor, I keep thinking I'm a mosquito.
Go away, sucker.

Doctor, doctor, I keep seeing an insect spinning round.
Don't worry, it's just a bug that's going round.

Centipede: Doctor, doctor, when my feet hurt, I hurt all over.

Doctor, doctor, I keep thinking I'm a nit.
Oh, get out of my hair!

Doctor, doctor, I keep thinking I'm a bee.
Oh, buzz off!

Doctor, doctor, I keep thinking I'm a butterfly?
Will you say what you mean and stop flitting about?

Doctor, doctor, I keep thinking I'm a caterpillar.
Don't worry, you'll soon change.

Doctor, doctor, I keep thinking I'm a spider.
What a web of lies!

Doctor, doctor, I keep thinking I'm a moth.
Get out of the way, you're in my light.

Waiter, waiter! There's a fly in my soup.
What do you expect for two dollars, sir? A beetle?

Waiter, waiter! There's a flea in my soup.
Tell him to hop it.

Waiter, waiter! There's a fly in my soup!
Yes, sir, he's committed insecticide.

Waiter, waiter! There's a fly in my custard.
I'll fetch him a spoon, sir.

Waiter, waiter! There's a cockroach on my steak.
They don't seem to care what they eat, do they, sir?

Waiter, waiter! There's a maggot in my salad.
Don't worry, he won't live long in that stuff.

Waiter, waiter! There's a spider in my soup.
It's hardly deep enough to drown him, sir.

Waiter, waiter! There's a wasp in my pudding.
So that's where they go to in the winter.

Waiter, waiter! There's a dead spider in my soup.
Yes, madam, they can't stand the boiling water.

Waiter, waiter! There's a fly in my soup.
Yes, that's the manager, sir. The last customer was a witch doctor.

Waiter, waiter! There's a fly in my wine.
Well, you did ask for something with a little body, sir.

Waiter, waiter! There's a fly in my soup.
Yes, madam, it's the bad meat that attracts them.

Waiter, waiter! What's this dead fly doing on my meat?
I don't know, madam, it must have died after tasting it.

Waiter, waiter! There's a spider in my soup. Send for the manager!
It's no good, sir, he's frightened of them too.

Waiter, waiter! What's this spider doing in my alphabet soup?
Probably learning to read, sir.

Waiter, waiter! What's this fly doing in my soup?
The butterfly stroke by the look of it, sir.

Waiter, waiter! There's a mosquito in my soup.
Don't worry, sir, mosquitoes have very small appetites.

Waiter, waiter! There's a beetle in my soup.
Sorry, sir, we're out of flies today.

Waiter, waiter! There's a fly in the butter.
Yes, sir, it's a butterfly.

Waiter, waiter! There's a fly in my soup.
Don't panic, sir. I'll call the RSPCA.

Waiter, waiter! There's a fly in my soup!
Don't worry, sir, the spider in your bread will get it.

Waiter, waiter! There's a bee in my alphabet soup.
Yes, sir, and I hope there's an A, a C and all the other letters too.

Waiter, waiter! There are two flies in my soup.
That's alright, sir. Have the extra one on me.

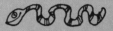

Waiter, waiter! What's this spider doing in my soup?
Trying to save the fly from drowning by the look of it, sir.

Waiter, waiter! There's a spider in my salad.
Yes, sir, the chef's using Webb lettuces today.

Waiter, waiter! What's this cockroach doing on my ice-cream sundae?
I think it's skiing downhill.

Waiter, waiter! There's a fly in my soup.
Just a minute, sir, I'll get the fly spray.

What kind of ant is good at adding up?
An account-ant.

What medicine do you give a sick ant?
Antibiotics.

What do you call an ant with five
pairs of eyes?
Ant-ten-eye.

Who is the most royal ant?
Princess Ant.

Why did the ant-elope?
Nobody gnu.

What's worse than ants in your pants?
A bat in your bra.

What kind of ant can you color with?
A cray-ant.

What game do ants play with monsters?
Squash.

What do you call an ant who can't
play the piano?
Discord-ant.

What do you get if you cross an
ant with half a pair of knickers?
Pant.

What do you call an ant that likes
to be alone?
An Independ-ant.

What do you call an ant with frog's legs?
An ant-phibian.

If ants are such busy insects, how come they find the time to turn up to picnics?

What do you call a hundred-year-old ant?
An antique.

Why don't anteaters get sick?
Because they're full of anty-
bodies!

Who was the most famous French
ant?
Napoleant.

What's the biggest ant in the
world?
An eleph-ant.

What is even bigger than that?
A gi-ant.

What do you call an ant who lives
with your great-uncle?
Your great-ant.

What is smaller than an ant's
mouth?
An ant's dinner.

How many ants are needed to fill
an apartment?
Ten-ants.

Who was the most famous
scientist ant?
Albert Antstein.

Where do ants eat?
In a restaur-ant.

What do you call ant space
travelers?
Cosmon-ants.

What do you call a smart ant?
Eleg-ant.

What kind of ants are very
learned?
Ped-ants.

What do you call a foreign ant?
Import-ant.

Where do ants go for their
holidays?
Fr-ants.

What do you call a greedy ant?
An anteater.

What do you call a scruffy, lazy ant?
Decad-ant.

What do you get if you cross some ants with some ticks?
All sorts of antics.

What do you call an ant who honestly hates school?
A tru-ant.

What has fifty legs but can't walk?
Half a centipede.

Why did the insects drop the centipede from their football team?
It took him so long to put his boots on.

Why do centipedes make such poor footballers?
By the time they've put their boots on, the match is nearly over.

What's worse than a giraffe with a sore throat?
A centipede with chilblains.

What goes ninety-nine clonk, ninety-nine clonk?
A centipede with a wooden leg.

Centipede to pal: I just hate it when I start the day off on the wrong foot.

What do you call a guard with 100 legs?
A sentrypede.

Why was the centipede late?
Because she was playing This Little Piggy with her baby.

What do you get if you cross a centipede with a parrot?
A walkie-talkie.

What is worse than a crocodile with toothache?
A centipede with athlete's foot.

What do you get if you cross a centipede with a chicken?
Enough drumsticks for an army.

What did one centipede say to another?
You've got a lovely pair of legs, pair of legs, pair of legs. . .

What has 100 legs and goes in one ear and out the other?
A centipede in a corn field.
(geddit?)

What kind of wig can hear?
An earwig.

What did the earwig say when it fell down the stairs?
Ear we go!

Why don't the other insects like earwigs?
Because they're always earwigging their conversations.

Where is Spiderman's home page?
On the World Wide Web.

What did the big weevil say to the little weevil?
You're the lesser of two weevils.

What happened when the chef found a daddy-long-legs in the lettuce?
The insect became daddy-short-legs.

Why did the spider buy a car?
He wanted to take it out for a spin.

What's red and dangerous?
Raspberry and tarantula jelly.

What did the spiders say to the fly?
We're getting married. Do you want to come to the webbing?

What did Mrs Spider say to Mr Spider when he broke her new web?
Darn it!

What does a spider do when he gets angry?
He goes up the wall.

How do you know if a spider is with it?
He doesn't have a web, he has a website.

What are spiders' webs good for?
Spiders.

Why do spiders enjoy swimming?
They have webbed feet.

What's a spider's favorite TV show?
The Newly-Web Game.

What do you call a big Irish spider?
Paddy-long-legs.

What would happen if tarantulas were as big as horses?
If one bit you, you could ride it to hospital.

Why are spiders like tops?
They're always spinning.

Where do spiders go for fun?
To Webley.

What has eight legs and likes
living in trees?
Four anti-road protesters.

What kind of doctors are spiders
like?
Spin doctors.

What do you call a hundred
spiders on a tyre?
A spinning wheel.

What did Mrs Spider say to
Mr Spider when he explained why
he was home late?
You're spinning me a yarn.

What pillar doesn't hold a building up?
A caterpillar.

What does a cat go to sleep on?
A caterpillow.

What's green and dangerous?
A caterpillar with a hand-grenade.

What does a caterpillar do on New
Year's Day?
Turns over a new leaf.

What is a grasshopper?
An insect on a pogo stick.

What's the definition of a
caterpillar?
A worm in a fur coat.

What is green and sooty and
whistles when it rubs its back legs
together?
Chimney Cricket.

What is green and can jump a mile
a minute?
A grasshopper with hiccoughs.

What do you call a grasshopper
with no legs?
A grass-hover.

Why is it better to be a grasshopper
than a cricket?
Because grasshoppers can play
cricket but there's no such game
as grasshopper.

What do you call a flea that lives in
an idiot's ear?
A space invader.

What do you get if you cross a flea
with a rabbit?
A bug's bunny.

How do you start an insect race?
One, two, flea, go!

What's the difference between a
flea and a coyote?
One prowls on the hairy, the other
howls on the prairie.

What did the clean dog say to the insect?
Long time, no flea!

What's a flea's favorite science fiction book?
The Itch-hiker's Guide to the Galaxy.

What do you call a flea that lives in Russia?
A Moscow-ito.

How do you find out where a flea has bitten you?
Start from scratch.

Why did the stupid boy wear a turtleneck sweater?
To hide his flea collar.

What's the difference between fleas and dogs?
Dogs can have fleas but fleas can't have dogs.

Why was the mother flea feeling
down in the dumps?
Because she thought her children
were all going to the dogs.

Who rides a dog and was a
Confederate general during the
American Civil War?
Robert E. Flea.

What did the idiot do to the flea in
his ear?
Shot it!

What did one flea say to another
after a night out?
Shall we walk home or take a dog?

Two fleas were running across the
top of a packet of soap powder.
"Why are we running so fast?"
gasped one.
"Because it says, 'Tear Along the
Dotted Line'."

What is the most faithful insect on
the planet?
Fleas. Once they find someone
they like they stick to them.

If a flea and a fly pass each other,
what time is it?
Fly past flea.

How do fleas keep in touch?
They send each other flea mails.

What do you call a cheerful flea?
A hop-timist.

What insect runs away from
everything?
A flee.

Waiter, waiter! There's a dead fly in
my soup.
Oh no! Who's going to look after
his family?

Waiter, waiter! What's this creepy crawly thing doing in my lettuce? I think he's trying to get out, madam.

Waiter, waiter! What's this creepy crawly thing doing in my dinner? Oh, that one – he comes here every night.

Waiter, waiter! What's this creepy crawly thing doing waltzing round my table?
It's the band, sir, it's playing his tune.

Waiter, waiter! What's this creepy crawly thing doing on my wife's shoulder?
I don't know – friendly thing, isn't he?

Waiter, waiter! There's a fly in my starter. Get rid of it, would you?
I can't do that, sir, he hasn't had his main course yet.

Waiter, waiter! There's a teeny beetle in my broccoli.
I'll see if I can find a bigger one, madam.

Waiter, waiter! There's a fly in my soup.
Go ahead and eat him. There are plenty more where he came from.

Sir, you haven't touched your custard.
No, I'm waiting for the fly to stop using it as a trampoline.

Waiter, waiter! There's a fly in my soup!
Just wait until you see the main course.

Waiter, waiter! There's a dead fly swimming in my soup.
Nonsense, sir, dead flies can't swim.

Waiter, waiter! There's a fly in my soup.
And what's the problem, sir?
I ordered slug soup.

Waiter, waiter! What kind of insect is this I've found in my dinner?
I don't know, sir, I can't tell one breed from another.

Waiter, waiter! There's a fly in my bean soup.
Don't worry, sir, I'll take it back and exchange it for a bean.

Waiter, waiter! What's this fly doing in my ice-cream?
Maybe he likes winter sports.

Why do waiters prefer monsters to flies?
Have you ever heard anyone complaining of a monster in their soup?

Two ants were watching a useless golfer swing wildly, trying to hit the ball. One said to the other, "Come on, let's get on the ball before he hits us."

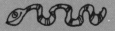

Two mosquitoes were buzzing round when they saw a drunken man. One said to the other, "You bite him – I'm driving."

A flea jumped over the swinging doors of a saloon, drank three whiskeys and jumped out again. He picked himself up from the dirt, dusted himself down and said, "OK, who moved my dog?"

Wicked Witches

What did the witch call her baby
daughter?
Wanda.

What did one witch say to the
other when they came out of the
cinema?
"Do you want to walk home or shall
we take the broom?"

What's a witch's favorite book?
Broom at the Top.

What's a witch's cat's favorite pop group?
Atomic Kitten.

Why did the witch join Tottenham Hotspur Football Club?
She heard they needed a new sweeper.

What makes more noise than an angry witch?
Two angry witches.

What do little witches like to play
at school?
Bat's cradle.

What happened to the witch with
an upside-down nose?
Every time she sneezed her hat
blew off.

What happened when the baby
witch was born?
It was so ugly its parents ran away
from home.

What happened when the witch
went for a job as a TV presenter?
The producer said she had the
perfect face for radio.

What kind of music do witches
play on the piano?
Hag-time.

What is old and ugly and can see
just as well from both ends?
A witch with a blindfold.

What do witches eat for
breakfast?
Rice Krispies because they snap at
them.

What do witches eat for dinner?
Real toad in the hole.

What is the best way of stopping
infection from witch bites?
Don't bite any witches.

What should you expect if you drop
in on a witch's home unexpectedly?
Pot luck.

What does a witch do if her broom
is stolen?
She calls the Flying Squad.

What do you call a witch who
climbs up walls?
Ivy.

Where do the cleanest witches
live?
Bath.

What do you call a witch with one leg?
Eileen.

How can you tell if a witch has a glass eye?
When it comes out in conversation.

What goes "cackle, cackle, bonk?"
A witch laughing her head off.

What is a witch's motto?
I came, I saw, I conjured.

How can you make a witch itch?
Take away her "W."

How does a witch tell the time?
With her witch watch.

What are little witches good at at
school?
Spelling.

How does a witch-doctor ask a girl
to polka with him?
Voodoo like to dance with me?

What do you call a nervous witch?
A twitch.

Who's the fastest witch?
The one that rides on a vroooooom
stick.

Why do witches fly on broomsticks?
Because vacuum cleaners are too
heavy.

What do you get if you cross a
sorceress with a millionaire.
A very witch person.

What kind of tests do they give in witch school?
Hex-aminations.

How do witches on broomsticks drink their tea?
Out of flying saucers.

Where does a witch keep her purse?
In a hag bag.

What do witches ring for in a hotel?
B-room service.

What kind of jewelry do warty witches wear on their wrists?
Charm bracelets.

What happens if you are confronted with two identical hags?
You can't tell witch is witch.

How do you know that you're in bed with a witch?
She has a big "W" embroidered on her pajamas.

When should you feed witch's milk to a baby?
When it's a baby witch.

What is a little witch after she is one year old?
A two-year-old witch.

What do you call a witch who
drives really badly?
A road hag.

What is another term for a witch?
A hag lady.

What do you call a witch who is
made of cotton and has lots of
holes in her?
A string hag.

What do you call a witch in a
horsehair shirt?
Itchy witchy.

Why should men be careful of
beautiful witches?
They'll sweep them off their feet.

Is it true that a witch won't hurt you
if you run away from her?
It all depends on how fast you run!

Why do witches have pointed hats?
Because they have pointed heads.

Why do some witches eat raw
meat?
Because they don't know how to
cook.

How do you make a witch float?
Take two scoops of ice cream, a
glass of Coke and one witch.

What type of boats do witches
sail?
Cat-amarans.

What's yellow and very poisonous?
Witch-infested custard.

Why did the witch buy two tickets
to the zoo?
One to get in and one to get out.

What do baby witches play with?
Deady bears.

How can you tell when witches are carrying a time bomb?
You can hear their brooms tick!

How do warty witches keep their hair out of place?
With scare spray.

Why is "s" the witches' favorite letter?
Because it turns cream into scream.

What do you call a pretty and
friendly witch?
A failure.

Why are witches' fingernails never
more than eleven inches long?
Because if they were twelve inches
they'd be a foot.

What do you call a witch who flies
in Concorde?
Lucky.

What is evil and ugly, puts spells on people and is made of leaves?
A witch (the leaves were just a plant).

What do you do with a blue witch?
Try to cheer her up.

What does a witch turn into when the lights go out?
The dark.

Why do witches go to the docks?
To see the bats being launched.

What do you do if a witch in a
pointy hat sits in front of you in the
cinema?
Miss most of the film.

How is a witch's face like a million
dollars?
It's all green and wrinkly.

What's evil and ugly and goes up
and down all day?
A witch in a lift.

Why did the witches go on strike?
Because they wanted sweeping
reforms.

What's the difference between a
witch and the letters m, a, k, e,
and s?
One makes spells and the other
spells makes.

Who went into a witch's den and
came out alive?
The witch.

What do you call two witches who
share a broomstick?
Broom-mates.

What do witches use pencil
sharpeners for?
To keep their hats pointed.

What is evil, ugly and keeps the
neighbors awake?
A witch with a drumkit.

Why do witches have stiff joints?
They get broomatism.

Why did the witch ride on a French
duster?
She felt like a dust-up.

When a witch falls into a pond
what is the first thing that she
does?
Gets wet.

What would you say if you saw nine
witches in black capes flying south
and one witch in a red cape flying
north?
That nine out of ten witches wear
black capes.

Are you getting sick of witch jokes?
Then cancel your subscription to witch.

What do you call it when a witch's
cat falls off her broomstick?
A catastrophe.

What do you get if you cross a
witch's cat with Father Christmas?
Santa Claws.

How do you get milk from a witch's
cat?
Steal her saucer.

What do witches' cats like for breakfast?
Mice Krispies.

What do you get if you cross a witch's cat with a canary?
A peeping tom.

What are baby witches called?
Halloweenies.

What does a witch enjoy cooking
most?
Gnomelettes.

Why is a witch's kitten like an
unhealed wound?
Both are a little pussy.

What do you call a witch's cat that
drinks vinegar?
A sour puss.

What do you call a witch's cat who
never comes when she's called?
Im-puss-able.

What has four legs, a tail, whiskers
and flies?
A dead witch's cat.

What do you get if you cross a
witch's cat and a canary?
A cat with a full tummy.

1st boy: Are you having a party for your birthday?

2nd boy: No, I'm having a witch do.

1st boy: What's a witch do?

2nd boy: She flies around on a broomstick casting spells.

1st witch: I spend hours in front of the mirror admiring my beauty. Do you think that's vanity?

2nd witch: No, it's imagination.

Witch: I have the face of a 16-year-old girl.
Wizard: Well you'd better give it back, you're making it all wrinkly.

Did you hear about the Daffy Duck witch?
She kept having Disney spells.

Which wizard never goes to the barber?
Hairy Potter.

1st witch: I went to the beauty parlor yesterday. I was there for three hours.
2nd witch: Oh, what did you have done?
1st witch: Nothing, I was just going in for an estimate.

What do you call a wizard with dandruff?
A blizzard.

Witch: You should keep control of your little boy. He just bit me on the ankle.
Vampire: That's only because he couldn't reach your neck.

1st witch: Have you tried one of these new paper cauldrons?
2nd witch: Yes.
1st witch: Did it work?
2nd witch: No, it was tearable.

1st witch: Shall I buy black or blue candles?

2nd witch: Which one burns longer?

1st witch: Neither, they both burn shorter.

A gang of witches broke into a blood bank last night and stole a thousand pints of blood. Police are still hunting for the clots.

Monster Books and Knock Knock Jokes

What did the monster say when he ate Aesop?
Make a fable out of that then!

What do ogres use to write with?
Ball point men.

The Bad-Tempered Werewolf – by
Claudia Armoff

The Greediest Monster in the World – by Buster Gutt

The Monster Hanging off the Cliff – by Alf Hall

The Hungry Yeti – by Aida Lot

Tracking Monsters – by Woody Hurt

I Met An Abominable Snowman –
by Anne Tarctic

Monsters I Have Known – by
O. Penjaw

When to go Monster Hunting – by
Mae B. Tomorrow

Bungee Jumping with Monsters –
by Wade R. Go

A Very Hungry Giant – by Ethan
D. Lot

I Caught the Loch Ness Monster –
by Janet A. Big-Wun

Knock Knock.
Who's there?
King Kong.
King Kong who?
King Kong's now part of China.

Knock Knock.
Who's there?
Turner.
Turner who?
Turner round, there's a monster
breathing down your neck.

Knock Knock.
Who's there?
Herman.
Herman who?
Herman Munster.

Knock Knock.
Who's there?
Oliver.
Oliver who?
Oliver lone and I'm frightened of
monsters.

Knock Knock.
Who's there?
Murphy.
Murphy who?
Murphy, have murphy! Don't eat
me!

Knock Knock.
Who's there?
Cecile.
Cecile who?
Cecile th-the w-windows. Th-there
is a m-monster out there.

Knock Knock.
Who's there?
Aida.
Aida who?
Aida whole village 'cos I'm a
monster.

Knock Knock.
Who's there?
Adair.
Adair who?
Adair you to open this door and
see my fangs.

Knock Knock.
Who's there?
Fido.
Fido who?
Fido known you were coming I'd
have bolted all the doors.

Knock Knock.
Who's there?
Reuben.
Reuben who?
Reuben my eyes 'cos I can't
believe what a big monster you are.

Knock Knock.
Who's there?
Teheran.
Teheran who?
Teheran very slowly – there's a
monster behind you.

Knock Knock.
Who's there?
Chile.
Chile who?
Chile being an abominable
snowman!

Knock Knock.
Who's there?
Kenya.
Kenya who?
Kenya save me from the
monsters?

Knock Knock.
Who's there?
Ghana.
Ghana who?
Ghana get me a gun and shoot
that werewolf.

How to Feed Werewolves – by Nora Bone

What's a man-eating monster's favorite book?
Ghouliver's Travels.

What lives in Tibet and spends too long on the phone?
A yak.

Dracula

How do vampire footballers get the mud off?
They all get in the bat-tub.

What do you call a dog owned by Dracula?
A blood hound.

Why does Dracula have no friends?
Because he's a pain in the neck.

What did the vampire do to stop
his son biting his nails?
He cut all his fingers off.

What was the Californian hippie
vampire like?
He was ghoul man. Real ghoul.

What's a vampire's favorite sport?
Batminton.

What happened to the two mad vampires?
They both went a little batty.

What do vampires cross the sea in?
Blood vessels.

What do vampires have at eleven o'clock every day?
A coffin break.

Where do vampires go on holiday?
To the Isle of Fright.

What do vampire footballers have
at half-time?
Blood oranges.

What do vampires like that are red
and very silly?
Blood clots.

How does Dracula like to have his
food served?
In bite-sized pieces.

What do vampires make
sandwiches out of?
Self-raising dead.

Why did the vampire take up
acting?
It was in his blood.

What is Count Dracula's least favorite song?
Vampire's Burning, Vampire's Burning.

What happened when a doctor crossed a parrot with a vampire?
It bit his neck, sucked his blood and said, "Who's a pretty boy then?"

Why did the vampire baby stop
having baby food?
He wanted something to get his
teeth into.

What happened to the lovesick
vampire?
He became a neck-romancer.

What do you get if you cross a
vampire with a snail?
I don't know but it would slow him
down.

Which vampire ate the three bears'
porridge?
Ghouldilocks.

Which vampire tried to eat James
Bond?
Ghouldfinger.

Why did the vampire go to
hospital?
He wanted his ghoulstones
removed.

Why did the vampire stand at the bus-stop with his finger up his nose?
He was a ghoulsniffer.

What does a vampire say when you tell him a ghoul joke?
Ghoul blimey!

What's Dracula's favorite dance?
The fang-dango.

When do vampires bite you?
On Wincedays.

What's a vampire's favorite drink?
A Bloody Mary.

What do vampires think of blood
transfusions?
New-fang-led rubbish.

Why did the vampire enjoy ballroom
dancing?
He could really get into the vaultz.

What happened at the vampires'
race?
They finished neck and neck.

Where did vampires go to first in
America?
New-fang-land.

What did Dracula say to the
Wolfman?
You look like you're going to the
dogs.

What do you get if you cross
Dracula with Al Capone?
A fangster.

Where do Chinese vampires come
from?
Fanghai.

What do vampires sing on New
Year's Eve?
Auld Fang Syne.

What do vampires have for lunch?
Fangers and mash.

What happened at the vampires'
reunion?
All the blood relations went.

What is Dracula's favorite fruit?
Neck-tarines.

Why did Dracula go to the dentist?
He had fang decay.

Why did he have fang decay?
He was always eating fangcy
cakes.

If you want to know more about Dracula what do you have to do?
Join his fang club.

What is the American national day for vampires?
Fangsgiving Day.

Why are vampire families so close?
Because blood is thicker than water.

How do vampires keep their breath smelling nice?
They use extractor fangs.

What does Dracula say when you tell him a new fact?
Well, fangcy that!

Why was Dracula thought of as polite?
He always said fangs.

Why did the vampire attack the clown?
He wanted the circus to be in his blood.

Did you know that Dracula wants to become a comedian?
He's looking for a crypt writer.

Which flavor ice cream is Dracula's favorite?
Vein-illa.

What is the first thing that
vampires learn at school?
The alphabat.

Why did Dracula go to the
orthodontist?
He wanted to improve his bite.

Why is Hollywood full of vampires?
They need someone to play the bit
parts.

Why do vampires like school dinners?
Because they know they won't get stake.

Why wouldn't the vampire eat his soup?
It clotted.

Why are vampires always exhausted in April?
Because they've just completed a long March of 31 days.

Why did the vampire sit on a pumpkin?
It wanted to play squash.

Did you hear about the boxer who went looking for Dracula?
He was out for the count.

What is a vampire's favorite soup?
Scream of tomato.

What's the difference between a vampire and a biscuit?
Have you ever tried dunking a vampire in your tea?

What do you get if you cross a vampire with a jar of peanut butter?
A vampire that sticks to the roof of your mouth.

What do you get if you cross a Rolls-Royce with a vampire?
A monster that attacks expensive cars and sucks out their gas tanks.

How do you join the Dracula Fan Club?
Send your name, address and blood group.

What happened when two vampires
went mad?
They went bats.

What's the vampire's favorite
song?
Fangs for the Memory.

What's a vampire's favorite animal?
A giraffe.

What do you get if you cross
Dracula with Sir Lancelot?
A bite in shining armor.

Why was the young vampire a
failure?
Because he fainted at the sight of
blood.

Why did the vampire give up
acting?
He couldn't find a part he could
get his teeth into.

What happened to the vampire who swallowed a sheep?
He felt baaaaaaaaaaaaad.

What does Mrs Dracula say to Mr Dracula when he leaves for work in the evening?
Have a nice bite!

What's Dracula's favorite coffee?
De-coffin-ated.

What's Dracula's car called?
A mobile blood unit.

Why do vampires do well at school?
Because every time they're asked
a question they come up with a
biting reply.

What is the vampire's favorite
slogan?
Please Give Blood Generously.

What do you get if you cross a vampire with a circus entertainer? Something that goes straight for the juggler.

What did the vampire say when he had been to the dentist?
Fangs very much.

Which space movie stars Count Dracula?
The Vampire Strikes Back.

How does a vampire clean his house?
With a victim cleaner.

Where is Dracula's American office?
The Vampire State Building.

Where do vampires keep their savings?
In blood banks.

What does the postman take to vampires?
Fang mail.

What did the vampire sing to the doctor who cured him of amnesia?
Fangs for the Memory.

What does a vampire stand on after taking a shower?
A bat mat.

What's a vampire's favorite dance?
The vaults.

What do romantic vampires do?
Neck.

Why was the vampire heartbroken?
His love was in vein.

What do you call a vampire junkie?
Count Drugula.

What did the vampire call his false teeth?
A new fangled device.

What did Dracula say to his new apprentice?
We could do with some new blood around here.

Why do vampires hate arguments?
Because they make themselves
cross.

What happened when the vampire
went to the bloodbank?
He asked to make a withdrawal.

What's a vampire's favorite love
song?
How Can I Ignore the Girl Necks
Door.

What does a vampire say to the mirror?
Terror, terror on the wall.

What's a vampire's favorite cartoon character?
Batman.

What did Dracula call his daughter?
Bloody Mary.

Why do vampires eat in transport cafes?
They can eat in them for necks to nothing.

What type of people do vampires like?
O positive people.

What do vampires play poker for?
High stakes.

Fish and Sea Creatures

Why did the slippery eel blush?
Because the sea weed.

What goes straight up in the air
and wobbles?
A jellyfishcopter.

How do you start a jellyfish race?
Get set!

What do you get if you cross an
octopus with a skunk?
An octopong.

How did the octopus lovers walk
down the road?
Arm in arm in arm in arm in arm in
arm in arm in arm.

What do you get if you cross a
jellyfish with a sheepdog?
Colliewobbles.

What did the octopus say to his moneylender?
Here's the sick squid I owe you.

What do octopuses play in their spare time?
Name that tuna.

What do you call a neurotic octopus?
A crazy, mixed-up squid.

What does an octopus wear when
it's cold?
A coat of arms.

What do you get if you cross a
bottle of water with an electric
eel?
A bit of a shock really!

What do you get if you cross an eel
with a shopper?
A slippery customer.

223

What's slimy, wobbly, tastes of
raspberry and lives in the sea?
A red jellyfish.

What do you get if you cross a
jellyfish with an elephant?
Jelly the Elephant.

What is wobbly, slimy and white
with red spots?
A jellyfish with measles.

One goldfish to his tankmate: If there's no God, who changes the water?

Why did the jellyfish's wife leave him?
He stung her into action.

What do you get if you cross an electric eel and a sponge?
Shock absorbers.

Why won't prawns share their toys?
Because they're shellfish.

How do eels get around the
seabed?
They go by octobus.

What's wet and wiggly and says
"How do you do" sixteen times?
Two octopuses shaking hands.

What is an eel's favorite song?
Slip Sliding Away.

Have you heard the joke about the slippery eel?
You wouldn't grasp it.

What is a sea monster's favorite dish?
Fish and ships.

What did the jellyfish say when she saw the electric eel?
How shocking!

What is an octopus?
An eight-sided cat.

There once was a lonely young
   jellyfish.
Who then met a sweet, loving
   shellyfish.
They went with the motion
Of waves in the ocean.
And became better known as the
   jollyfish.

Girl: Do you know what family the octopus belongs to?
Boy: No one in our street.

Did you hear about the man who tried to cross the Loch Ness Monster with a goat?
He had to get a new goat.

Did you hear about the stupid jellyfish?
It set!

Knock Knock.
Who's there?
Eel.
Eel who?
Eel meet again.

Doctor, doctor, I feel like an electric
eel.
That's shocking.

What happened when one jellyfish
met another?
They produced jelly babies.

One day, a boy was walking down the street when he saw a sea monster standing on the corner looking lost. The boy put a lead on the sea monster and took him to the police station. "You should take him to the museum," said the police sergeant.

The next day the police sergeant saw the boy in the town still with the monster on a lead. "I thought I told you to take him to the museum," said the policeman.

"I did," said the boy, "and today I'm taking him to the movies."

What do you get if you cross the
Loch Ness Monster with a shark?
Loch Jaws.

What eats its victims two by two?
Noah's Shark.

How do you communicate with the
Loch Ness Monster at 20,000
fathoms?
Drop him a line.

What fish tastes best with cream?
A jellyfish.

Teacher: Martin, put some more
water in the fish tank.
Martin: But, sir, they haven't drunk
the water I gave them yesterday.

What sort of fish performs
surgical operations?
A sturgeon.

Mrs Turbot, the biology teacher, was very fond of fish. She was also rather deaf, which was great for the children in her class. What Mrs Turbot needs, said one of her colleagues, is a herring-aid.

The vampire went into the Monster Cafe. "Shark and chips," he ordered. "And make it snappy."

Werewolves

Mommy, Mommy, what's a
werewolf?
Shut up John and comb your face.

Why was the werewolf arrested in
the butcher's shop?
He was chop-lifting.

What parting gift did a mommy
werewolf give to her son when he
left home?
A comb.

237

Where does a werewolf sit in the theater?
Anywhere he wants to!

What do you get if you cross a witch with a werewolf?
A mad dog that chases airplanes.

What do you get when you cross a werewolf with a drip-dry suit?
A wash-and-werewolf.

What happened when the werewolf chewed a bone for an hour? When he got up he only had three legs.

How do you know that a werewolf's been in the fridge? There are paw prints in the butter.

How do you know that two werewolves have been in the fridge?
There are two sets of paw prints in the butter.

What does it mean if there is a werewolf in your fridge in the morning?
You had some party last night!

Did you hear about the comedian who entertained at a werewolves' party?
He had them howling in the aisles.

Did you hear about the sick werewolf?
He lost his voice but it's howl right now.

What TV program do werewolves
never miss?
Fiends.

What did the werewolf say after
he finished writing a book?
I hope it's a howling success.

What do you get if you cross a
hairdresser with a werewolf?
A monster with an all-over perm.

What happened when the werewolf
swallowed a clock?
He got ticks.

How do you make a werewolf stew?
Keep him waiting for two hours.

Why did the boy take an aspirin
after hearing a werewolf howl?
Because it gave him an eerie
ache.

Why shouldn't you grab a werewolf by its tail?
It might be the werewolf's tail but it could be the end of you.

I used to be a werewolf but I'm all right noooooooooooooooooow!

How do you stop a werewolf attacking you?
Throw a stick and shout fetch!

Why are werewolves thought of as quick-witted?
Because they always give snappy answers.

Why did the mommy and daddy werewolves call their son Camera?
Because he was always snapping.

What do you call a hairy beast with clothes on?
A wear-wolf.

What do you call a hairy beast in a river?
A weir-wolf.

What do you call a hairy beast that no longer exists?
A were-wolf.

What do you call a hairy beast that's lost?
A where-wolf.

What happens if you cross a
werewolf with a sheep?
You have to get a new sheep.

What's fearsome, hairy and drinks
from the wrong side of a glass?
A werewolf with hiccoughs.

What did the werewolf write at the
bottom of the letter?
Best vicious . . .

What happened when the werewolf
met the five-headed monster?
It was love at first fright.

How do you stop a werewolf
howling in the back of a car?
Put him in the front.

Animal Antics

Why is a frog luckier than a cat?
Because a frog croaks all the time
– a cat only croaks nine times.

What would you get if you crossed
a frog with a little dog?
A croaker spaniel.

What is the definition of a narrow
squeak?
A thin mouse.

What goes eek, eek, bang?
A mouse in a minefield.

What's gray and squeaky and
hangs around in caves?
Stalagmice.

What's the hardest part about
milking a mouse?
Getting the bucket underneath it.

Who is the king of all the mice?
Mouse Tse Tung.

What do angry rodents send each
other at Christmas?
Cross mouse cards.

Which mouse was a Roman
emperor?
Julius Cheeser.

Hickory, dickory, dock,
The mice ran up the clock.
The clock struck one,
And the rest got away with minor
   injuries.

What is gray and hairy and lives on
a man's face?
A mousetache.

What's gray and furry on the
inside and white on the outside?
A mouse sandwich.

What do you call a mouse that can
pick up a monster?
Sir.

How do mice celebrate when they
move house?
With a mouse-warming party.

What did the mouse say when his
friend broke his front teeth?
Hard cheese.

Why did the mouse eat a candle?
For light refreshment.

What is a mouse's favorite game?
Hide and squeak.

What goes "dot, dot, dash, squeak"?
Mouse code.

What is white one minute and
brown the next?
A rat in a microwave oven.

Who has large antlers, a high voice
and wears white gloves?
Mickey Moose.

What do you get if you cross a
sheep with a space ship?
Apollo neck jumper.

What is brown one minute and
white the next?
A rat in a deep-freeze.

What do you get if you cross a
mouse with a packet of soap
powder?
Bubble and Squeak.

How do rabbits keep their fur
neat?
They use a harebrush (hairbrush).

What is small, furry and smells like
bacon?
A hamster.

Why do mice need oiling?
Because they squeak.

What is a mouse's favorite record?
Please Cheese Me.

What's a rat's least favorite
record?
What's up, Pussycat?

How do you save a drowning
rodent?
Use mouse-to-mouse
resuscitation.

What kind of musical instrument
do rats play?
Mouse organ.

How can you tell the difference
between a rabbit and a red-eyed
monster?
Just try getting a red-eyed
monster into a rabbit hutch.

Why was the Abominable
Snowman's dog called Frost?
Because Frost bites.

What has six legs and flies?
A witch giving her cat a lift.

Why are cats such good singers?
They're very mewsical.

When is it unlucky to see a black cat?
When you're a mouse.

How can you tell that a cat likes rain?
Because when it rains it purrs (pours).

How can you keep a barking dog quiet?
With hush puppies.

Why was the little horse unhappy?
Because every time it wanted something, its mother would say, "Neigh."

Why is a pig's tail like 5 a.m.?
They are both twirly (too early).

What does a duck wear when he
gets married?
A duxedo (tuxedo).

Why was the horse all charged up?
Because it ate haywire.

Why do black cats never shave?
Because eight out of ten cats
prefer Whiskas.

What kind of cattle laugh?
Laughing stock.

How do pigs write?
With a pigpen.

What kind of cats like to go
bowling?
Alley cats.

Now you see it . . . now you don't –
What are you looking at?
A black cat walking over a zebra
crossing.

What bone will a dog never eat?
A trombone.

What has four legs, a tail, whiskers
and goes round and round for
hours?
A black cat in a tumble-drier.

What has four legs, a tail, whiskers
and cuts grass?
A lawn miaower.

For pigs, what came after the
Stone Age and the Bronze Age?
The sausage.

What do you call a witch's cat with
no legs?
Anything you like – she won't be
able to come anyway.

What is a black cat's favorite TV
program?
Miami Mice.

What's furry, has whiskers and
chases outlaws?
A posse cat.

Ding, dong, bell,
Pussy's down the well,
But we've put some disinfectant
  down
And don't mind about the smell.

What do witches' cats strive for?
Purr-fection.

What do you call a witch's cat who
can spring from the ground to her
mistress's hat in one leap?
A good jum-purr.

What do you call a witch's cat who
can do spells as well as her
mistress?
An ex-purr-t.

How does a pig go to hospital?
In a hambulance.

Why did the skeleton run up a
tree?
Because a dog was after its
bones.

What does a unicorn call its
father?
Popcorn.

What did Dr Frankenstein get
when he put his goldfish's brain in
the body of his dog?
I don't know, but it is great at
chasing submarines.

There once was a very strong cat
Who had a fight with a bat.
The bat flew away
And at the end of the day
The cat had a scrap with a rat.

What's white, fluffy and floats?
A cat-emeringue.

Mother: Keep that dog out of the house, it's full of fleas.
Son: Keep out of the house, Fido, it's full of fleas.

Wizard: Have you put the cat out?
Witch: Was he burning again?

Customer: I'd like a mousetrap, please.
Assistant: Have you tried Boots?
Customer: I'd like to catch it, not kick it to death.

1st Witch: My boyfriend's gone and stolen my black cat.
2nd Witch: You mean your familiar.
1st Witch: Well, we were, but I'm not speaking to him now.

Witch: Doctor, doctor, I keep thinking I'm my own cat.

Doctor: How long have you thought this?

Witch: Since I was a kitten.

Emm: What's the name of your dog?

Nik: Ginger.

Emm: Does Ginger bite?

Nik: No, but Ginger snaps.

What's got four legs, barks and
goes "tick tock"?
A watch dog.

How do you make a hot dog stand?
Steal its chair.

What's the difference between a
flea-bitten dog and a bored
visitor?
One's going to itch. The other's
itching to go.

A workman had just finished laying a carpet in a witch's house when he realised he had lost his sandwiches. Looking round he saw a lump under the carpet. Not wanting to pull the carpet up again he just got a big plank of wood and smashed the lump flat. Then the witch came into the room with a cup of tea for him. "Here's your tea," she said. "My, you've laid the carpet well. Just one thing, though, have you seen my pet toad anywhere?"

What would you have discovered if
you found bones on the moon?
The cow didn't make it.

What is a zebra?
Twenty-six sizes larger than an
"A" bra.

What do you get from a pampered
cow?
Spoiled milk.

"Won't you let me live one of my own lives?" said the put-upon young cat to its parents.

A blind rabbit and a blind snake ran into each other on the road one day. The snake reached out, touched the rabbit and said, "You're soft and fuzzy and have floppy ears. You must be a rabbit." The rabbit reached out, touched the snake and said, "You're slimy, beady-eyed and low to the ground. You must be a math teacher."

Why did a man's pet vulture not
make a sound for five years?
It was stuffed.

What happened to the skeleton
that was attacked by a dog?
The dog ran off with some bones
and left him without a leg to stand
on.

What did one black cat say to the other?
Nothing. Cats can't speak.

What did the black cat do when its tail was cut off?
It went to a re-tail store.

What do you get when a vampire bites a rat?
A neighborhood free of cats.

Two monsters went duck-hunting with their dogs but without success. "I know what we're doing wrong," said the first one.
"What's that then?" said the second.
"We're not throwing the dogs high enough!"

"Mary," said her teacher, "you can't bring that lamb into school. What about the smell?"
"Oh, that's all right, Miss," said Mary. "It'll soon get used to it."

Mouse I: I've trained that crazy science teacher at last.

Mouse II: How have you done that?

Mouse I: I don't know how, but every time I run through that maze and ring the bell, he gives me a piece of cheese.

It's obvious that animals are smarter than humans. Put eight horses in a race and 20,000 people will go along to see it. But put eight people in a race and not one horse will bother to go along and watch.

Why is it easy to swindle a sheep?
Because you can just pull the wool
over its eyes.

There was once a puppy called May
who loved to pick quarrels with
animals who were bigger than she
was. One day she argued with a
lion. The next day was the first of
June. Why? Because that was the
end of May!

Is it hard to bury an elephant?
Yes, it's a huge undertaking.

My dog saw a sign that said: Wet
Paint – so he did!

My dog is a nuisance. He chases
everyone on a bicycle. What can I
do?
Take his bike away.

What's an American cat's favorite car?
A Catillac.

A man went into the local department store where he saw a sign on the escalator – Dogs must be carried on this escalator. The man then spent the next two hours looking for a dog.

What sort of fish would you find in a shoe?
An eel.

"I'm sorry to call you out at this time of night," said the witch, "but it's my poor black cat. He's just lying there telling me he wants to die."
The monster vet licked his lips.
"Well, you've done the right thing by sending for me."

Teacher: And did you see the Catskill Mountains on your visit to America?

Jimmy: No, but I saw them kill mice.

A motorist approached the principal one afternoon and said, "I'm awfully sorry, but I think I've just run over the school cat. Can I replace it?"

The principal looked him up and down and replied, "I doubt if you'd be the mouser she was."

Why was the monkey taken in for
questioning?
Because they wanted to gorilla.

What's a twip?
What a wabbit calls a twain ride!

What happened when the
headmistress's poodle swallowed
a roll of film?
Nothing serious developed.

A man out for a walk came across
a little boy pulling his cat's tail.
"Hey, you!" he called. "Don't pull
the cat's tail!"
"I'm not pulling!" replied the little
boy. "I'm only holding on – the cat's
doing the pulling!"

Why were the elephants kicked out
of the swimming pool?
Because they kept dropping their
trunks in the water.

Did you hear about the witch who
fed her pet vulture on sawdust?
The vulture laid ten eggs and
when they hatched, nine chicks
had wooden legs and the tenth
was a woodpecker.

Caspar: I was the teacher's pet
last year.
Jaspar: Why was that?
Caspar: She couldn't afford a dog.

What do ghosts like about riding horses?
Ghoulloping.

Slithering Slimies and Revolting Reptiles

What did the snake say when he was offered a piece of cheese for dinner?
Thank you, I'll just have a slither.

What did one slug say to another who had hit him and rushed off?
I'll get you next slime!

How do you know your kitchen is filthy?
The slugs leave trails on the floor that read "Clean me."

What did the slug say as he slipped down the window very fast?
How slime flies!

What's the difference between school dinners and a pile of slugs?
School dinners come on a plate.

What is the strongest animal in the world?
A snail, because it carries its home on its back.

What do you do when two snails
have a fight?
Leave them to slug it out.

What is the definition of a slug?
A snail with a housing problem.

Where do you find giant snails?
On the end of a giant's fingers.

What do you get if you cross a
worm with a young goat?
A dirty kid.

What do you get if you cross a
glow-worm with a pint of beer?
Light ale.

Why was the glow-worm unhappy?
Because her children were not very
bright.

What did the woodworm say to the chair?
It's been nice gnawing you!

What's worse than finding a maggot in your apple?
Finding half a maggot in your apple.

What did one maggot say to another?
What's a nice girl like you doing in a joint like this?

What do you get if you cross a
glow-worm with a python?
A twenty-foot-long strip-light that
can squeeze you to death.

How can you tell if you are looking
at a police glow-worm?
He has a blue light.

When should you stop for a glow-
worm?
When he has a red light.

Why are glow-worms good to carry
in your bag?
They can lighten your load.

What's yellow, wiggly and
dangerous?
A maggot with a bad attitude.

What did one worm say to another
when he was late home?
Why in earth are you late?

What's the difference between a worm and a gooseberry?
Ever tried eating worm pie?

What do you get if you cross a worm with an elephant?
Big holes in your garden.

What is the best advice to give a worm?
Sleep late.

Why do worms taste like chewing gum?
Because they're Wrigley's.

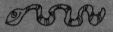

What lives in apples and is an avid reader?
A bookworm.

What makes a glow-worm glow?
A light meal.

What would you do if you found a
bookworm chewing your favorite
book?
Take the words right out of its
mouth.

What is a bookworm's idea of a big
feast?
War and Peace.

Who was wet and slippery and
invaded England?
William the Conger.

What is wet and slippery and likes
Latin American music?
A conga eel.

What do you get if you cross a
snake with a Lego set?
A boa constructor.

What is a snake's favorite food?
Hiss fingers.

What is the difference between a poisonous snake and a headmaster?
You can make a pet out of the snake.

Which hand would you use to grab a poisonous snake?
Your enemy's.

What do you do if you find a black mamba in your toilet?
Wait until he's finished.

What is a snake's favorite opera?
Wriggletto.

Why did the two boa constrictors
get married?
Because they had a crush on each
other.

What should you do if you find a
snake in your bed?
Sleep in the wardrobe.

What do you call a snake that is
trying to become a bird?
A feather boa.

Why can't you trust snakes?
They speak with forked tongue.

What snakes are good at sums?
Adders.

What do you get if you cross a
snake with a hotdog?
A fangfurter.

What is a snake's favorite dance?
Snake, rattle and roll.

What do you get if you cross a
snake with a pig?
A boar constrictor.

Why are snakes hard to fool?
They have no leg to pull.

What do you call a python with a
great bedside manner?
A snake charmer.

Why did the viper want to become
a python?
He got the coiling.

What do most people do when they
see a python?
They re-coil.

What school subject are snakes
best at?
Hiss-tory.

What did the snake say to the
cornered rat?
Hiss is the end of the line mate!

What do snakes have on their bath
towels?
Hiss and Hers.

What do you call a snake that
informs the police?
A grass-snake.

What did the python say to the
viper?
I've got a crush on you.

What did the mommy snake say to
the crying baby snake?
"Stop crying and viper your nose."

What's the best thing about
deadly snakes?
They've got poisonality.

What's a snake's favorite dance?
The mamba.

What's a snake's second favorite dance?
The shuffle.

What do you get if you cross two snakes with a magic spell?
Addercadabra and abradacobra.

What did one snake say when the other snake asked him the time?
Don't asp me!

What do you give a sick snake?
Asp-rin.

What would you get if you crossed
a new-born snake with a basket-
ball?
A bouncing baby boa.

What kind of letters did the snake
get from his admirers?
Fang mail.

What's long and green and goes
hith?
A snake with a lisp.

Why did some snakes disobey
Noah when he told them to go
forth and multiply?
They couldn't – they were adders.

Which snakes are found on cars?
Windscreen vipers.

What's the definition of a nervous
breakdown?
A chameleon on a tartan rug.

What kind of tiles can't you stick
on the wall?
Rep-tiles.

What do you call a rich lizard?
A gold-blooded reptile.

What kind of bull doesn't have
horns?
A bullfrog.

What jumps up and down in front
of a car?
Froglights.

Where does a ten-tonne frog
sleep?
Anywhere it wants to!

When is a car like a frog?
When it's being toad.

What did one frog say to the other?
Time's sure fun when you're having flies!

What did the lobster say to the rock pool?
Show me your mussels.

What do you get if you cross a
compass with a shellfish?
A guided mussel.

Why did the toad become a
lighthouse keeper?
He had his own frog-horn.

What do you call a frog who wants
to be a cowboy?
Hoppalong Cassidy.

Why do frogs have webbed feet?
To stamp out forest fires.

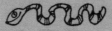

What is a frog's favorite dance?
The Lindy Hop.

What do frogs sit on?
Toadstools.

What happens to illegally parked frogs?
They get toad away.

What do you say if you meet a toad?
Wart's new?

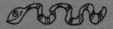

Why did the lizard go on a diet?
It weighed too much for its scales.

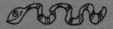

Why did the crab get arrested?
Because he was always pinching
things.

What did the croaking frog say to
his friend?
I think I've got a person in my
throat.

What's green and goes round and
round at 60 miles an hour?
A frog in a liquidizer.

What is yellow and goes round and round at 60 miles an hour?
A mouldy frog in a liquidizer.

Why was the frog down-in-the-mouth?
He was un-hoppy.

What happened to the prawn that went to a disco?
It pulled a mussel.

How do frogs die?
They Kermit suicide.

Why doesn't Kermit like
elephants?
They always want to play leap-frog
with him.

What do you get if you cross a
planet with a toad?
Star warts.

What is a toad's favorite ballet?
Swamp Lake.

What do toads drink?
Croaka-cola.

What do frogs drink?
Hot croako.

What is green and slimy and is
found at the North Pole?
A lost frog.

What kind of shoes do frogs like?
Open toad sandals.

What do you call a frog spy?
A croak and dagger agent.

Where do frogs keep their treasure?
In a croak of gold at the end of the rainbow.

What do you get if you cross a toad with a mist?
Kermit the Fog.

What do you call a girl with a frog on her head?
Lily.

How did the toad die?
It simply croaked.

What do you call someone who makes half-size models of fish?
A scale modeller.

What's the weakest animal in the world?
A toad. He will croak if you touch him.

Where do toads leave their coats
and hats?
In the croakroom.

What is green and tough?
A toad with a machine gun.

What's white on the outside, green
on the inside and comes with
relish and onions?
A hot frog.

What happens if you eat a hot frog?
You croak in no time.

What is the chameleon's motto?
A change is as good as a rest.

What kind of pole is short and floppy?
A tadpole.

What do you call a skeleton snake?
A rattler.

Keeping Pet Snakes – by Sir Pent

Collecting Reptiles – by Ivor Lizard

Collecting Wriggly Creatures – by
Tina Worms

There once was a snake named
Drake
Who started a fight with a rake.
It cut off his tail
Drake went very pale
And that's the short end of my
tale.

There was an old man called Jake
Who had a poisonous snake.
It bit his head
And now he's dead
So that was the end of Jake.

A boa with coils uneven
Had the greatest trouble in
breathing.
With jokes she was afflicted
For her laughs got constricted
And her coils started writhing and
wreathing.

A cobra was invited to dine
By his charmingly cute valentine.
But when he got there
He found that the fare
Was pineapple dumplings with
wine.

334

1st person: I've just been bitten by a snake on one arm.

2nd person: Which one?

1st person: I don't know, one snake looks very much like the next one.

How do you catch elephant fish? Use peanuts for bait.

1st snake: I'm glad I'm not poisonous!

2nd snake: Why?

1st snake: Because I've just bitten my tongue.

Fisherman: What are you fishing for sonny?

Boy: I'm not fishing, I'm drowning worms.

Surveyor: This house is a ruin. I wonder what stops it from falling down?

Owner: I think the woodworm are holding hands.

Boy: What's black, slimy, with hairy legs and eyes on stalks?

Mom: Eat the biscuits and don't worry what's in the tin.

How does a lobster answer the
phone?
"Shello?"

Witch: I'd like some tiles for my
bathroom.
Shopkeeper: But this is a pet shop.
Witch: That's all right – I want
reptiles.

Did you hear about the stupid snake?
He lost his skin.

Did you hear about the stupid woodworm?
He was found in a brick.

Did you hear about the glow-worm that didn't know if it was coming or glowing?

Did you hear about the beautiful ancient Greek termite that lunched a thousand ships?

Knock Knock.
Who's there?
Thumping.
Thumping who?
Thumping green and slimy is creeping up your leg.

Knock Knock.
Who's there?
Maggot.
Maggot who?
Maggot me this new dress today.

Knock Knock.
Who's there?
Worm.
Worm who?
Worm in here isn't it?

Knock Knock.
Who's there?
Snake.
Snake who?
Snake a run for it!

Knock Knock.
Who's there?
Adder.
Adder who?
Adder you get in here?

Knock Knock.
Who's there?
Viper.
Viper who?
Viper your nose!

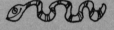

Knock Knock.
Who's there?
Python.
Python who?
Python with your pocket money.

Knock Knock.
Who's there?
Woodworm.
Woodworm who?
Woodworm cake be enough or
would you like two?

Knock Knock.
Who's there?
Crispin.
Crispin who?
Crispin crunchy frog sandwich.

Doctor, doctor, I think I'm turning into a frog.
Oh, you're just playing too much croquet.

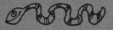

Doctor, doctor, I keep thinking I'm a python.
Oh you can't get round me like that, you know.

Doctor, doctor, I keep thinking I'm an adder.
Oh good, could you help me with my tax return?

Doctor, doctor, I keep thinking I'm a toad.
Go on, hop it!

Doctor, doctor, I keep thinking I'm a snail.
Don't worry, we'll soon have you out of your shell.

Doctor, doctor, I feel like an insignificant worm.
Next!

346

Doctor, doctor, I keep thinking I'm a snake about to shed its skin.
Just slip into something more comfortable.

Waiter, waiter! There's a slug in my salad.
I'm sorry, sir, I didn't know you were a vegetarian.

Waiter, waiter! There's a slug in my dinner.
Don't worry, sir, there's no extra charge.

Waiter, waiter! There's a slug in my lettuce.
Sorry madam, no pets allowed here.

Waiter, waiter! There's a worm in my soup.
That's not a worm, sir, that's your sausage.

Waiter, waiter! Have you got frogs' legs?
No, sir, I always walk like this.

Waiter, waiter! Do you serve snails?
Sit down, sir, we'll serve anyone.

Waiter, waiter! Do you have frogs' legs?

Yes sir.

Well then hop into the kitchen for my soup.

Waiter, waiter! Are there snails on the menu?

Oh yes, sir, they must have escaped from the kitchen.

Waiter, waiter! I can't eat this meat, it's crawling with maggots. Quick, run to the other end of the table, you can catch it as it goes by.

A woman walked into a pet shop and said, "I'd like a frog for my son."

"Sorry madam," said the shopkeeper. "We don't do part exchange."

Why couldn't the whales make themselves understood to the angry porpoises?
Because they were speaking at cross porpoises.

What's gray, eats fish and lives in Washington DC?
The Presidential Seal.

What did the witch say to the ugly toad?
I'd put a curse on you – but somebody beat me to it!

What were the only creatures not to go into the ark in pairs?
Maggots. They went in an apple.

What do you get if you cross a frog with a decathlete?
Someone who pole-vaults without a pole.

1st Witch: I like your toad. He always has such a nice expression on his face.
2nd Witch: It's because he's a hoptimist.

Spook: Should you eat spiders and slugs and zombie slime on an empty stomach?
Witch: No, you should eat them on a plate.

Naughty Knock Knock Jokes

Knock Knock.
Who's there?
Hawaii.
Hawaii who?
Hawaii getting on?

Knock Knock.
Who's there?
Haydn.
Haydn who?
Haydn the shed.

Knock Knock.
Who's there?
Muffin.
Muffin who?
Muffin to declare.

Knock Knock.
Who's there?
Munro.
Munro who?
Munro fast to the other side.

Knock Knock.
Who's there?
Bacon.
Bacon who?
Bacon a cake in the oven.

Knock Knock.
Who's there?
Juan.
Juan who?
Juance upon a time there were
three bears.

Knock Knock.
Who's there?
Roland.
Roland who?
Roland stone gathers no moss.

Knock Knock.
Who's there?
Little old lady.
Little old lady who?
I didn't know you could yodel.

Knock Knock.
Who's there?
Liz.
Liz who?
Lizen carefully, I will say this only once.

Knock Knock.
Who's there?
Sorrel.
Sorrel who?
Sorrel about the mess.

Knock Knock.
Who's there?
Soup.
Soup who?
Souper Mom!

Knock Knock.
Who's there?
Venice.
Venice who?
Venice this going to end?

Knock Knock.
Who's there?
Verdi.
Verdi who?
Verdia want to go?

Knock Knock.
Who's there?
You.
You who?
Who's that calling out?

Knock Knock.
Who's there?
Zippy.
Zippy who?
Zippydidooda, zippydeeay!

Knock Knock.
Who's there?
Juicy.
Juicy who?
Juicy what I see?

Knock Knock.
Who's there?
July.
July who?
July or do you tell the truth?

Knock Knock.
Who's there?
Debbie.
Debbie who?
Debbie or not to be.

Knock Knock.
Who's there?
Debussy.
Debussy who?
Debussy's never on time.

Knock Knock.
Who's there?
Egg.
Egg who?
Eggsactly.

Knock Knock.
Who's there?
Egypt.
Egypt who?
Egypt me out in the cold!

Knock Knock.
Who's there?
Norway.
Norway who?
Norway is this your house – it's so big!

Knock Knock.
Who's there?
Nose.
Nose who?
Nosinging in the house.

Knock Knock.
Who's there?
Scott.
Scott who?
Scott land the brave.

Knock Knock.
Who's there?
Scully.
Scully who?
Scully-wag!

Knock Knock.
Who's there?
Census.
Census who?
Census presents for Christmas.

Knock Knock.
Who's there?
Cereal.
Cereal who?
Cereal pleasure to meet you.

Knock Knock.
Who's there?
Organ.
Organ who?
Organize a party – it's my birthday.

Knock Knock.
Who's there?
Orson.
Orson who?
Orson, let your daddy in.

Knock Knock.
Who's there?
Roxie.
Roxie who?
Roxie Horror Show.

Knock Knock.
Who's there?
Royal.
Royal who?
Royal show you his paintings if you
ask nicely.

Knock Knock
Who's there?
Voodoo.
Voodoo who?
Voodoo you think you are?

Knock Knock.
Who's there?
Walter.
Walter who?
Walter wall.

Knock Knock.
Who's there?
Russia.
Russia who?
Russia down the shops before
they close.

Knock Knock.
Who's there?
Ryder.
Ryder who?
Ryder fast horse.

Knock Knock.
Who's there?
Yellow.
Yellow who?
Yellowver the din – I can't hear you.

Knock Knock.
Who's there?
Yoga.
Yoga who?
Yoga what it takes!

Knock Knock.
Who's there?
Iran.
Iran who?
Iran all the way here. Let me in!

Knock Knock.
Who's there?
Ivana.
Ivana who?
Ivana be alone.

Knock knock.
Who's there?
Ben Hur.
Ben Hur who?
Ben Hur an hour – let me in.

Knock knock.
Who's there?
Benin.
Benin who?
Benin hell.

Knock Knock.
Who's there?
Alma.
Alma who?
Almany times do I have to knock?

Knock Knock.
Who's there?
Althea.
Althea who?
Althea in court.

Knock Knock.
Who's there?
Berlin.
Berlin who?
Berlin maiden over.

Knock Knock.
Who's there?
Bertha.
Bertha who?
Bertha day boy.